Introduction

The day it began was a day like any other. The sun came up and smiled, the air was filled with the sound of birdsong and the trees were beginning to breathe out the sweet scent of spring. But inside our homes, we could only look and wonder at the life outside through our window panes. Each one of us, all around the globe, had to stay at home. It was lockdown and we were all in it together. On my short walks every day, where I walked the dog, I made space for my neighbours. My children found new ways to play as playgrounds shut their gates, and grass grew high and long around the abandoned slides and swings. But I found beauty in the silence, too. Empty streets were filled with big billboards thanking our keyworkers. I noticed fewer aeroplanes interrupted the wide blue sky. At last, by standing still I could hear nature's movements, as wind rustled through the leaves and creatures called to one another in the quiet. I was not alone. Our communities held hands together, virtually and symbolically, and we made it through a point in time very few people have ever seen before. We ventured to our front doors and clapped for our hardworking keyworkers. We learned that there was a bright side to everything, that there was room for laughter, and that there was always, always, hope.

This book is all about humanity and resilience. We have asked Tiny Owl illustrators to reflect on their experiences in lockdown, focussing on what filled them with hope and joy during those difficult months. Inside, you will find 15 contributions from our wonderful illustrators. The pages showcase their distinctive styles, but the collective threads of kindness, positivity, and hope weave their way through every illustration. Whether you're reading *Unlocked* in one sitting or dipping in and out, each original drawing offers readers – both big and little – a ray of sunshine on a gloomy day, and a chance to reflect upon a truly unique year for us all!

We hope you are inspired.

Delaram Ghanimifard
Co-founder Tiny Owl Publishing

For teacher resources and more information, visit www.tinyowl.co.uk
#TinyOwlUnlocked

First published in the UK in 2021 by Tiny Owl Publishing, London.

Cover illustration © Anna Doherty 2021
Endpapers illustration © Sarah van Dongen 2021

UK ISBN 978-1-910328-76-7

UNLOCKED

Stories of hope from Tiny Owl artists
in lockdown

My daily walks were precious.
I avoided the normally busy streets
as the emptiness made me too sad.

But there is beauty in the quiet.
We discovered all sorts of amazing
green spaces very close to the house
we've lived in for years and years and
never noticed before.

We watched spring arrive in front
of a sleeping city, and found the
perfect trees to climb...

Jenny Bloomfield (UK)

Figo came to stay with me during lockdown.
Days were sweeter with him around.
Figo is very kind. He likes to eat, play, and go
outside. Everyday, I had to give him treats and play with
him to keep him busy. He, in turn, kept me busy too.

Ehsan Abdollahi (Iran)

We got up early in the morning and left the village with our walking sticks and hats. (Follow the red arrows to see where we went.)

We would take the farm road back home so we could greet our friends, the horses.

Then all the way to the
lighthouse at the very
Western tip of Europe.

We walked through the
forest, past the chapel by
the little stream, down-
hill through two villages.

We took the coastal path back and
ate our oranges on the beach.

Piet Grobler (Portugal)

My boyfriend and I decided
if we couldn't go out,
we'd bring the outside IN.
We imagined a cafe,
with a menu and loyalty card.

We imagined cinema days and
attended theatres and concerts.

We imagined a gym and yoga
studio in our living room.

We imagined a garden
and planted seeds.

As the world outside stood still, we watched the seasons change and new life grow inside.

Sarah van Dongen (Netherlands)

During lockdown I
practised baking.

Kate Milner (UK)

At first I missed my
'Grandma Jenny' hugs
and cuddles but then ...

Florence came over and
gave me a window 'high 5'

Tom floated his love to me

Ellie made me a noodle smile

And Hattie
sent a distanced
'good night' hug.

Jenny Duke (UK)

I worked more
than ever.

I talked to my friends and family more than ever.

I thought more than ever.

I worked out more than ever.

Nahid Kazemi (Iran – Canada)

One of the coolest things I experienced during lockdown was the music and song from the balconies and windows of my city. We all had more time to be creative, to try new things, to look out at the moon and stars shining down in the night sky.

I chatted with neighbours I'd never met before, we helped each other. We shared food, stories, support, and hope.

Dunja Jogan (Slovenia – Italy)

As spring turned to summer,
the dawn called me earlier
each day and I delighted in
a theatre of fresh bright
leaves, sliced through with
rays of bright sunshine.
A stage for a choir of
birdsong, accompanied by a
percussion of woodpeckers
and featuring the soprano
screech of excited squirrels.

Hazel Terry (UK)

I made jars of kimchi.
Lots of them.

The kimchi was red, but not too spicy.
I had them everyday, for breakfast, lunch, and dinner.

Maria Christania Winardi (Indonesia – UK)

kimchi cheese toast

Kimchi with rice

Kimchi stir fry

Kimchi fried rice

Just kimchi

Kimchi ramen

Kimchi omelette

Kimchi soup

I spent my time time in lockdown talking to the world,
just in a different way.

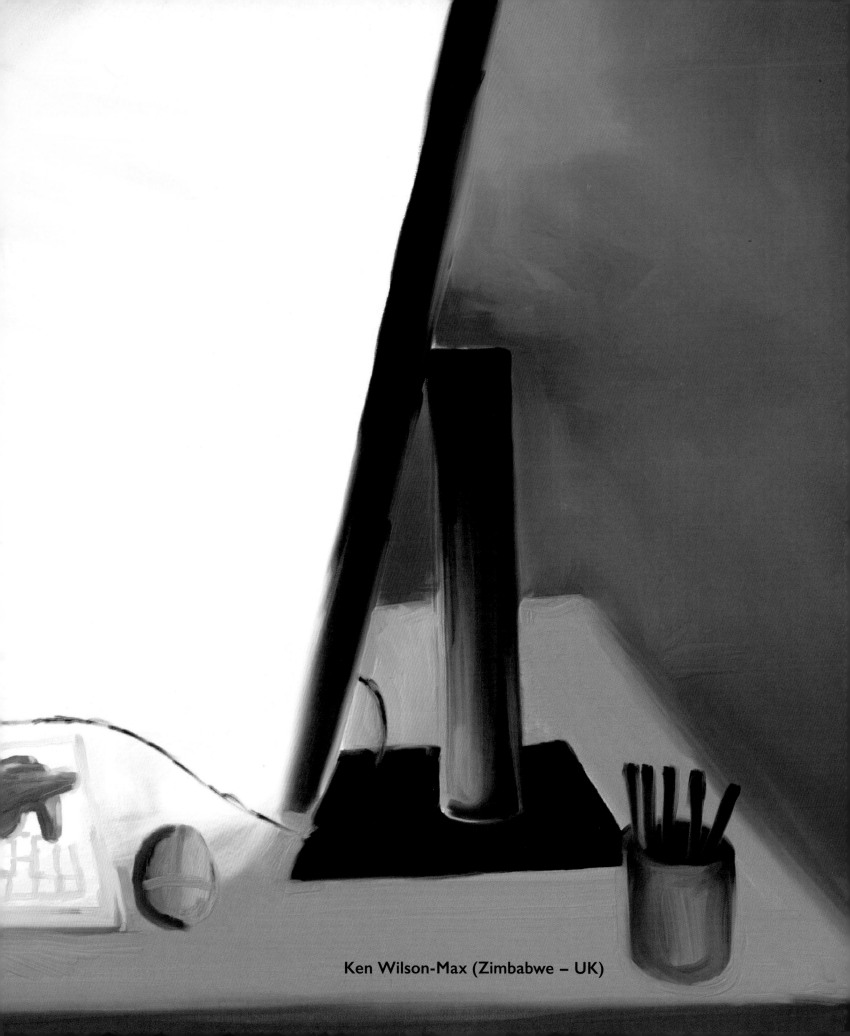

Ken Wilson-Max (Zimbabwe – UK)

One day, I decided to visit my local forest.

I hugged a tree who seemed
friendly and it felt very good.

Then I decided to sit down, close my eyes, and listen intently to all the sounds of the forest.

Soon, I felt as if I was being observed with great curiosity.

Catell Ronca (Switzerland)

We had a whole bunch of celebrations in lockdown over video calls: birthdays, graduations, and new jobs were celebrated.

We put on our party hats A LOT!

Anna Doherty (UK)

It's strange to have a party where everyone is in a different place — but you get to see what other people's houses look like. And everyone got to eat their own entire cake each time!

In lockdown I have been...
growing things,

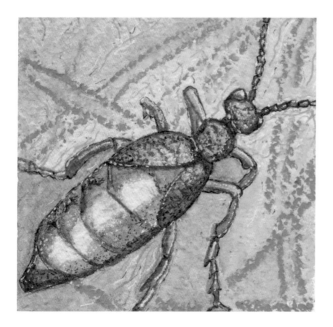

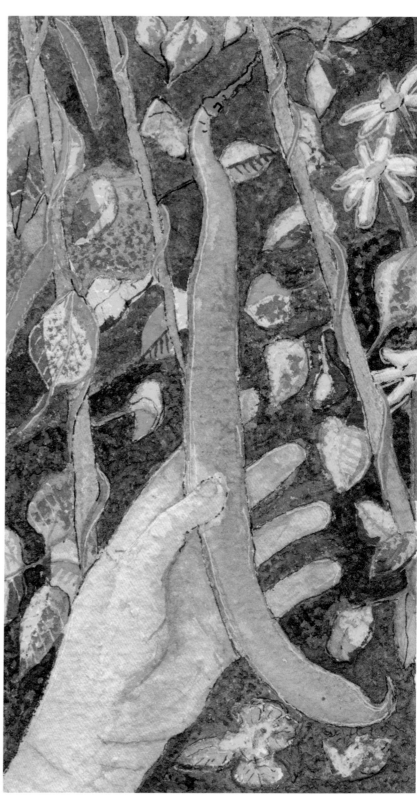

Nicola Davies (UK)

looking at the sky,
noticing the details,
and going where the
path leads.

I have learned that even without sunshine, the sea still sparkles.

Dale Blankenaar (South Africa)

I made a box for you to hide
with lines to keep you safe.
Inside there is a flowering field
and, eventually, an escape.

Unlocked Author Biographies

Jenny Bloomfield

Jenny Bloomfield completed an MA in Children's Book Illustration from Cambridge School of Art in 2019. Drawing and image making is what makes her happy every day. On her Instagram page, she has shared a new piece of art each day since September 2014! Jenny lives in Leeds with her husband, two children and an angry, fat cat called Pop-Pops. Her other work with Tiny Owl includes *We All Celebrate!* (2021).

Ehsan Abdollahi

Ehsan Abdollahi is an illustrator and animator, and teaches at Tehran Art University in Iran. He creates handmade and hand-coloured paper in his collages. His art is inspired by the environment and the fabrics from Southern Iran. His other books with Tiny Owl include *When I Coloured in the World* (2015), *A Bottle of Happiness* (2016), *Thinker: My Puppy Poet and Me* (2018), *The Secret of the Tattered Shoes* (2019).

Piet Grobler

Piet Grobler is an acclaimed, multi-award winning South African illustrator and author of over 80 wonderfully witty books for children. He now lives in sunny Portugal. He co-founded the International Centre for the Picture Book in Society, which he set up whilst Course Leader for Illustration at the University of Worcester. His other books with Tiny Owl include *Paris Cat* (2020).

Sarah Van Dongen

Sarah van Dongen is an author and illustrator, born in Rotterdam. After studying Literature in Utrecht and Amsterdam, she then completed an MA in Children's Book Illustration at Cambridge. She grew up with vegetable gardens, an orangery, a herd of deer, and plenty of green space to explore! Sarah's childhood still inspires her work today. Her other work with Tiny Owl includes her picture book debut *The Neighbourhood Surprise* (2021).

Hazel Terry

Hazel Terry is an author and illustrator living in Edinburgh. She has studied many different types of art, including Drawing and Painting at Edinburgh College of Art, and an MA in Illustration from the University of Hertfordshire. She uses all types of supplies and mediums in her art, creating beautiful designs with everyday objects. Her other work with Tiny Owl includes her picture book debut *Rock and Roll* (2021).

Maria Christania Winardi

Maria Christania Winardi grew up in Indonesia. She studied her degree in Visual Communication Design at Bandung Institute of Technology, before working as a freelance graphic designer and spending a few years teaching in a nursery. In 2014, she moved to the UK with her husband, before completing an MA in Children's Book Illustration at Cambridge School of Art. She currently lives in Milton Keynes, working part-time in a nursery, and dedicating her evenings to illustration.

Ken Wilson-Max

Ken Wilson-Max grew up in Zimbabwe. He travelled to the UK to study Design, and then began working in children's publishing. He has illustrated and worked on more than 60 books. Ken frequently works with children in schools and libraries, and also publishes a newspaper for children called *Chicken!* His other books with Tiny Owl include *The Drum* (2018) and *The Flute* (2019).

Catell Ronca

Catell lives and works in Lucerne, Switzerland. She graduated from the Royal College of Art in London and works for a variety of international clients in publishing, editorial and advertising. Her work is regularly recognised in illustration annuals. Some of her favourite things are the Swiss Alps, hand painted folk art, and making ceramic objects and tiles.

Kate Milner

Kate Milner is an author and illustrator, who has published many books. She completed an MA in illustration from Anglia Ruskin. She won the V&A Student Illustration Award in 2016 and the Klaus Flugge Prize in 2018. Her brilliant illustrations and prints have been published in magazines and exhibited in galleries across London. Her other books with Tiny Owl include *Sorry, Mrs Cake* (2021).

Jenny Duke

Jenny Duke has always loved books and making pictures. Before delving into the world of illustration, she worked with children, teachers, and museums. Since her MA in Children's Book Illustration at Cambridge University, she has been working on a number of projects, several based in East Anglia where the skies, water, and light inspire much of her work. Her books always begin by drawing, but she never knows where a project will take her until much later!

Nahid Kazemi

Nahid Kazemi has illustrated more than 50 books for children and received her MA from Tehran Art University. She has appeared at national and international festivals. She likes to explore collage and textiles within her work. She currently lives in Canada. Her other books with Tiny Owl include *Alive Again* (2015) and *The Orange House* (2016).

Dunja Jogan

Dunja Jogan is an artist and graphic designer who has published several books. Her work has been selected five times for the Italian Illustrators Annual. Originally from Slovenia, she currently lives in Trieste, Italy. Her book *Felix After the Rain* (2020) was awarded the English PEN Translates Award (2019), which allowed Tiny Owl to translate it from Slovenian.

Anna Doherty

Anna Doherty is an illustrator from sunny Scotland, now based in Cambridge. She adores drawing, writing, and every single dog in the world. Outside of illustration, her main skills in life are rock, paper, scissors, and swimming long distances under water without breathing! Her other books with Tiny Owl include *Fair Shares* (2019) and *Best Test* (2020).

Nicola Davies

Nicola Davies is an award-winning author of over fifty books, but it was with Tiny Owl that she dived into the wonderful world of illustration with her beautiful story *Last: The Story of the White Rhino* (2020)! Originally training as a zoologist, from the moment she could walk, she has been fascinated by animals, getting her first pair of binoculars for her eighth birthday. She was even one of the original presenters of the BBC's *The Really Wild Show*. She lives in Powys, Wales.

Dale Blankenaar

Dale Blankenaar is a picture book illustrator and designer from South Africa. He has illustrated over 30 picture books. He has won several international awards. In his work, he often loves to experiment with bright primary colours and explore different cultures, such the wood sculpture of West Africa. His other books with Tiny Owl include *Quill Soup* (2019).